Independent Schools
Examinations Board

FRENCH PRACTICE EXERCISES
13+

Joyce Čapek
and Nigel Pearce

Independent Schools
Examinations Board

www.galorepark.co.uk

GALORE PARK

Published by ISEB Publications, an imprint of Galore Park Publications Ltd
19/21 Sayers Lane, Tenterden, Kent TN30 6BW
www.galorepark.co.uk

Text copyright © Joyce Čapek and Nigel Pearce 2009

The right of Joyce Čapek and Nigel Pearce to be identified as the authors of
this work has been asserted by them in accordance with sections 77 and 78 of
the Copyright, Designs and Patents Act 1988.

Design and typesetting by Typetechnique
Printed by Replika Press, India

ISBN-13: 978 0903627 78 8

First published 2009. Reprinted 2010

Details of other ISEB Revision Guides for Common Entrance, examination
papers and Galore Park publications are available at www.galorepark.co.uk

Front cover photo: Mike Goldwater/Alamy

Illustrations on the following pages by Ian Douglass: p13 row 2C, row 5R; p14
row 2C'; p15 row 1C and R; p17 row 1 all, row 2L, row 4 all; p18 row 4L and
C; p19 row 1 all; p27; p32; p42 row 1L; p44 row 2R; p45 row 1; p46 row 2R.

The audio material referred to in this book is available as a download from
www.galorepark.co.uk. A CD version is also available ISBN 978 1 905735 396.

Introduction

Welcome to *French Practice Exercises 13+*! This Practice volume puts all the knowledge you have learned from your Common Entrance French course to the test. The Listening and Speaking practice and Reading and Writing exercises are set out in styles which you might reasonably expect to encounter in the French examinations you are going to be sitting. If you have successfully come this far,

Bravo. Bon courage. Bonne chance!

Acknowledgements

The authors wish to express their immense gratitude to the team at Galore Park for enabling the publishing of this work.

Nigel Pearce and Joyce Čapek, January 2009

Note: The instructions for each section are based on the syllabus for first examinations in Spring 2010. The changes to the syllabus include:

Listening

- Instructions will now be given in English.
- The range of test types will all be in English.
- Answers will all now be given in English.

Reading and Writing

Reading

- Instructions will now be given in English.

Writing

- Instructions will now be given in English.

Contents

Speaking

Role-play situation

Exercise 1.1 Au camping

You have arrived at a campsite, and approach the receptionist. SHE WILL SPEAK FIRST.

1. Ask if there's a place for a caravan.
2. Answer the question.
3. Ask if there's a shop on the site.
4. Ask if the village is far.
5. Ask if the shops are open on a Sunday.
6. Say thank you, and ask if you have to pay now.

Exercise 1.2 Vacances en Bretagne

You are in Brittany and telephoning a friend back home. HE WILL SPEAK FIRST.

1. Greet your friend, and say you're in Brittany.
2. No, you're camping.
3. Answer the question.
4. Yes, and there is a games room, tennis courts and a snack bar.
5. Say yes, you're five minutes from the beach.
6. Yes, you're really enjoying yourself.
7. You're staying for a fortnight. You're returning next Sunday.

Exercise 1.3 On réserve des chambres

You telephone a hotel to book a room, and speak to the receptionist.
SHE WILL SPEAK FIRST.

1. Greet the lady, and say you would like to make a reservation.
2. Say it's for three nights from 7th July.
3. Say there are three of you. You want one double room and one single.
4. Your name is Duclos. Spell it for her.
5. Answer the question.
6. Ask if the hotel has a car park.
7. Say that's excellent. Thank her and say goodbye.

Exercise 1.4 A la plage (a)

You are on a beach and a boy approaches you. HE WILL SPEAK FIRST.

1. Give your name.
2. Say no, you're on holiday.
3. Answer the question.
4. Say you have a little brother who is ten. He's playing over there.
5. No, he's the tall boy with black hair.
6. Say yes, it's great. You like to go swimming and wind-surfing.
7. Say yes, you'd like to.

Exercise 1.5 A la plage (b)

You are on a beach and a girl approaches you. SHE WILL SPEAK FIRST.

1. Say yes, you live in London. Ask her where she lives.
2. Say the countryside is lovely.
3. Say there's lots to do in London.
4. Answer the question.
5. Say it's fine, but your flat is very small and you don't have a garden.
6. Tell her she's lucky.

Exercise 1.6 Vacances à la montagne

A friend is asking you about your skiing holiday. SHE WILL SPEAK FIRST.

1. Say yes, you spent a week in the Alps.
2. No, you go there every year.
3. Answer the question.
4. Not bad, but your father skis better than you.
5. Say she loves skiing but unfortunately last year she broke her arm.

Exercise 1.7 A la gare

You are at the station. You go to the ticket office and approach the man working there.
HE WILL SPEAK FIRST.

1. Ask for a return ticket to Bordeaux.

2. Answer the question, and ask how much it is.

3. Hand over the money, then ask what time the next train leaves.

4. Ask if it's direct.

5. Ask which platform it leaves from.

6. Find out where the left-luggage office is.

7. Thank him.

Exercise 1.8 Dans le train

You strike up a conversation with a fellow passenger on the train.
SHE WILL SPEAK FIRST.

1. Say yes, and ask whether this seat is free.

2. Yes, you're going to your cousins in Biarritz.

3. Say no, you're English. Ask her if she knows England.

4. Say you live in a little village in the southwest of England.

5. In winter yes, but in summer the weather is lovely.

6. Answer the question.

7. Yes, you take the boat and train. The plane is much too expensive.

Exercise 1.9 Au téléphone

*Your friend rings you. **SHE WILL SPEAK FIRST.***

1. Greet her, and ask how she is.

2. Say you're well. Ask her if she's free on Saturday.

3. Say you have tickets for the match.

4. Ask her if she wants to come.

5. Answer the question.

6. Agree, and say you will see her on Saturday.

Exercise 1.10 Dans la rue

Somebody stops you in the street to ask directions. **SHE WILL SPEAK FIRST.**

1. Say it's quite far. You have to take the bus.

2. Say it's over there, outside the chemist's.

3. Say there's a tobacconist's just opposite.

4. Answer the question.

5. Say not at all.

Exercise 1.11 A la banque

You are in the bank, and approach the man working there. **HE WILL SPEAK FIRST.**

1. Say you would like to change some money.

2. Answer the question.

3. Ask if he would like to see your passport.

4. Oh dear, you haven't got your passport with you! You have left it in the hotel.

5. Say you will have to go back to the hotel. Ask what time they close.

6. Say you will hurry.

Exercise 1.12 Au café

You go into a café with a friend. **SHE WILL SPEAK FIRST.**

1. Say yes, if she wants. There's a table over there in the corner.

2. Answer the question.

3. Say yes. Ask what there is to eat.

4. Ask what that is.

5. Say very good, you will have* the same as her.

Exercise 1.13 Au restaurant

You are in a restaurant, and the waiter approaches. **HE WILL SPEAK FIRST.**

1. Ask what the dish of the day is.

2. Say that's fine. Order two set meals at 10 euros.

3. Answer the question, and say that your mother will have the raw vegetables.

4. Order a bottle of Beaujolais and some mineral water.

5. Tell the waiter politely that the fork is a bit dirty.

* Note that in French we would say 'take'.

4

Exercise 1.14 Au bureau des objets trouvés

You are in the lost property office, and approach the woman working there.
SHE WILL SPEAK FIRST.

1. Say yes, you hope so. You have lost your sports bag.
2. It's black and white with Nike on it.
3. Answer the question.
4. A white towel and green swimming trunks.
5. Oh yes! There's also a navy blue jumper.
6. Say yes it is, and thank her.

Exercise 1.15 Chez le médecin

You are in the surgery, and approach the doctor. HE WILL SPEAK FIRST.

1. Greet the doctor, and say you have a very sore throat.
2. Answer the question.
3. No, you haven't taken anything.
4. Say yes, a bit. You're also very hot.
5. Ask the doctor if it's flu.
6. Ask him if you should take something.
7. Thank the doctor.

Exercise 1.16 Je suis malade

You feel ill, and are talking to your friend. HE WILL SPEAK FIRST.

1. Say no, you're going to stay at home.
2. Say you don't feel very well.
3. You have a sore stomach.
4. Answer the question.
5. Say yes, and ask him if he can go to the chemist for you.

Exercise 1.17 A l'école

You are talking with a school friend. SHE WILL SPEAK FIRST.

1. Answer the question, and ask her what she has.
2. Say you're quite good at maths.
3. Say he's a bit boring. You prefer Mr Martin, your history teacher.
4. Ask your friend what she's doing after school. Does she want to come to the park?
5. Tell her she works too hard.
6. Say yes, and wish her a good day!

Exercise 1.18 Chez un correspondant (a)

You are visiting your French penfriend. SHE WILL SPEAK FIRST.

1. Say yes, the sea was calm fortunately!

2. You're not too tired. You slept a bit on the boat.

3. Say no, you've been once before with your parents.

4. Answer the question.

5. Say yes, very much. You had a good time.

6. Admire your penfriend's house.

7. Say no, it's all right. It's not too heavy.

8. Say yes please.

Exercise 1.19 Chez un correspondant (b)

You are having a meal with your French penfriend, and speak to your friend's mother. SHE WILL SPEAK FIRST.

1. Say it smells good.

2. Say you're hungry.

3. Say you don't know. You have never tried them.

4. Say yes, it's really delicious.

5. Yes, you would.

6. Answer the question.

Prepared topics

How the examination operates

Part A (1–2 minutes; 8 marks)

The candidate will choose any topic covered by the syllabus (see Appendix on page 51) or a topic in connection with a country where the target language is spoken, for example:

- a town or region
- a regional or national celebration
- an artist (painter, sculptor, writer, composer, etc.)
- an historical figure
- a sportsman/sportswoman.

The candidate should introduce his/her topic, with the teacher-examiner intervening after about 30 seconds to ask at least four questions during the course of the two minutes. Credit will be given for communication of information, pronunciation and intonation, range of vocabulary, range of grammar as set out in the syllabus, accuracy, fluency and readiness of response.

Part B (1–2 minutes; 8 marks)

The candidate will be required to speak about one of the following topic areas:

- house, home, daily routine and chores
- free time and holiday activities
- life and work at school
- personal description, family, friends and pets.

The teacher-examiner will choose the topic for each candidate and give him/her the title at the beginning of the preparation time. No candidate will receive the same topic for Part B as that chosen for Part A. The examiner will ask the candidate to introduce the topic in French. After about 30 seconds the examiner will intervene to ask at least four questions during the course of the two minutes. Credit will be given for relevant communication, appropriate response to the questions and quality of language, including pronunciation.

Speak in French for around 30 seconds on each topic by following the bullet points. Then play the CD track and answer the questions in French.

Exercise 2.1 Daily routine and work at school

In a presentation, describe a typical day at school. Talk about:

- when you get up in the morning
- what you eat and drink for breakfast, and where you have it
- what you do afterwards
- where you go
- how many lessons you have per day
- the subjects that you learn
- which subjects you like and don't like
- what you do in the evening before going to bed.

Exercise 2.2 Holiday activities

In a presentation, describe a day on holiday. Talk about:

- where you like to go on holiday
- what you eat and drink on holiday that you don't have at home
- where you go, and with whom.

Describe two or three things that you like to do on holiday. Talk about:

- your activities at home
- what you like to do on holidays abroad
- the disadvantages of some kinds of transport
- what you do in the evening before going to bed.

Exercise 2.3 Where you live

In a presentation, describe your house or flat. Talk about:

- how many rooms there are
- how many floors there are
- where the bedrooms are – which bedrooms are on which floors
- where the bathroom(s) and kitchen are
- what you do in your room
- whether there is a garden
- what you can do in the garden

- where you generally eat
- what you do to help around the house
- what you like and don't like about where you live.

Exercise 2.4 Your town

In a presentation, describe the town where you live, or a town nearby. Talk about:

- the shops
- the restaurants, if there are any
- whether there is a swimming pool, cinema, or sports facilities, etc.
- when you go into town, and with whom
- what you do in town.

Exercise 2.5 Your family

In a presentation, describe your family. Talk about:

- who you live with
- whether you have any brothers or sisters
- how old the members of your family are
- how you spend your time together.

Exercise 2.6 Free time

In a presentation, talk about what you like to do in your spare time. Talk about:

- what you do at home
- what you do outside (play tennis, for example)
- who you like to spend your spare time with
- why you like these activities.

Talk about what you have to do for these activities:

- how much they cost
- how long you have been doing them
- who else can do them (children, teenagers, adults?).

Listening

The following exercises, grouped by sections, are a selection from the varied styles listed above. They are all typical examples to be found in the exam. In each case, play the CD track and follow the instructions given in the question.

Exercise 3.1

Listen to the CD track and decide which picture matches the sentence, as in the example:

Je joue au tennis le mercredi.

   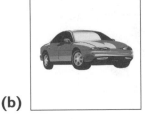   

(a)   (b)   (c)

Réponse: **(a)**

. . . .

1.

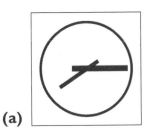   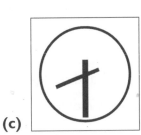

(a)   (b)   (c)

. . . .

2. (a)   (b)   (c)

3. (a)   (b)   (c)

4. (a)   (b)   (c)

5. (a)   (b)   (c)

Exercise 3.2

Listen to the CD track and decide which picture matches the sentence, as in the example:

Je joue au tennis le mercredi.

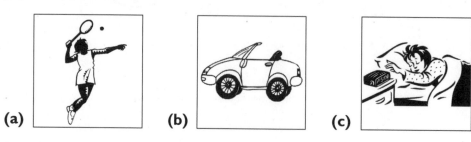

(a)   (b)   (c)

Réponse: **(a)**

1.

(a)   (b)   (c)

. . . .

2.

(a)   (b)   (c)

. . . .

3.

(a)   (b)   (c)

. . . .

4.

(a)   (b)   (c)

. . . .

5.

(a)   (b)   (c)

. . . .

Exercise 3.3

Listen to the CD track and decide which picture matches the sentence, as in the example:

J'aime écouter de la musique.

(a)

(b)

(c)

Réponse: **(a)**

1.

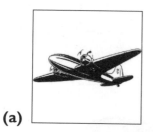

(a)

(b)

(c)

2.

(a)

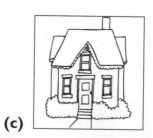

(b)

(c)

3.

(a)

(b)

(c)

14

4.

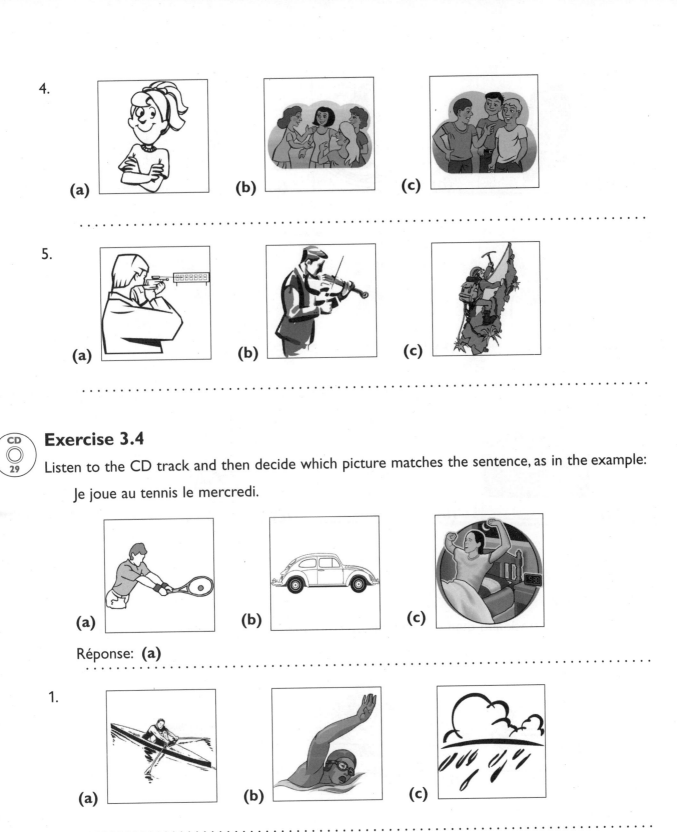

(a)   (b)   (c)

. . . .

5.

(a)   (b)   (c)

. . . .

Exercise 3.4

Listen to the CD track and then decide which picture matches the sentence, as in the example:

Je joue au tennis le mercredi.

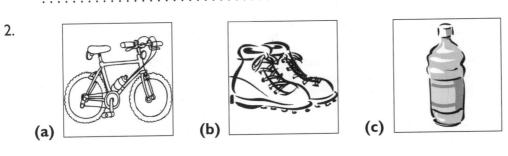

(a)   (b)   (c)

Réponse: (a)

. . . .

1.

(a)   (b)   (c)

. . . .

2.

(a)   (b)   (c)

. . . .

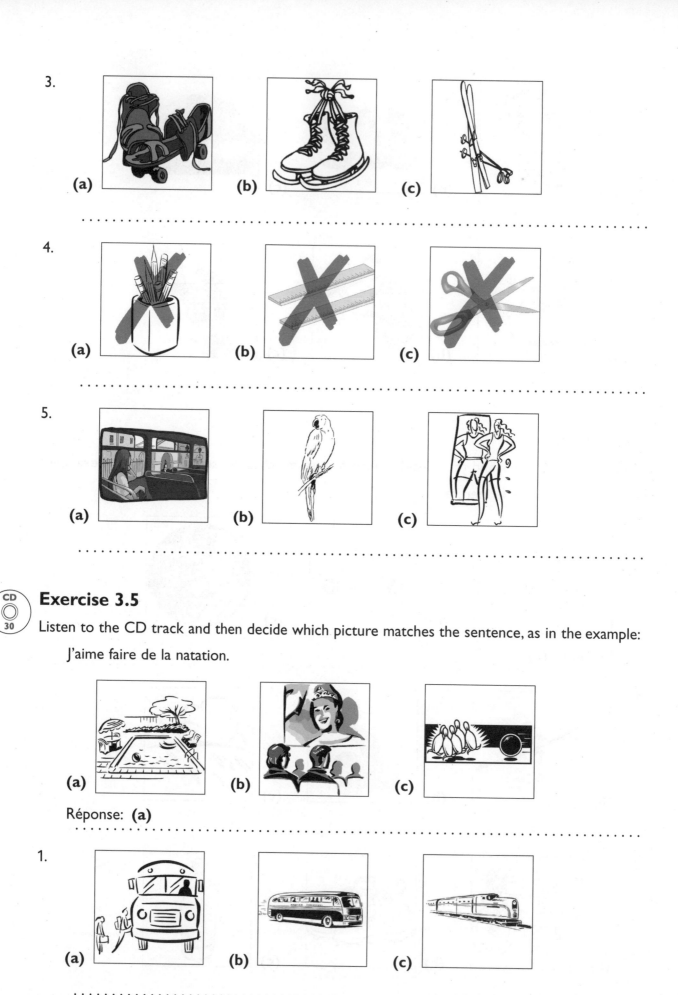

3.

   (a)   (b)   (c)

4.

   (a)   (b)   (c)

5.

   (a)   (b)   (c)

CD 30

Exercise 3.5

Listen to the CD track and then decide which picture matches the sentence, as in the example:

J'aime faire de la natation.

   (a)   (b)   (c)

Réponse: **(a)**

1.

   (a)   (b)   (c)

2.

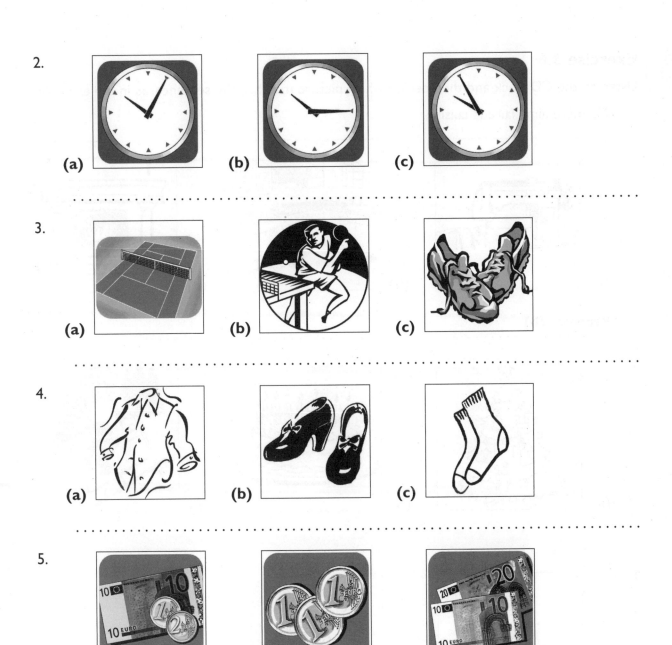

(a)   **(b)**   **(c)**

. . . .

3.

(a)   **(b)**   **(c)**

. . . .

4.

(a)   **(b)**   **(c)**

. . . .

5.

(a)   **(b)**   **(c)**

. . . .

Exercise 3.6

Listen to the CD track and then decide which picture matches the sentence, as in the example:

Ma mère aime faire la cuisine.

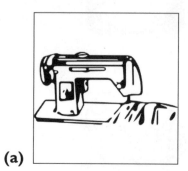

(a)   **(b)**    **(b)**    **(c)**

Réponse: **(b)**

. . . .

1.

(a)    **(b)**    **(c)**

. . . .

2.

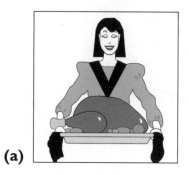

(a)    **(b)**   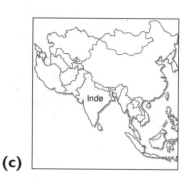 **(c)**

. . . .

3.

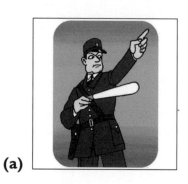

(a)   **(b)**    **(c)**

. . . .

4.

(a)   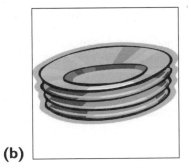 (b)    (c)

....

5.

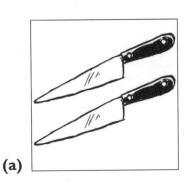

(a)   (b)    (c)

....

CD 32

Exercise 4.1   On prépare un pique-nique

Listen to the CD track and then write your answers in English.

1. The girl suggests having a picnic by the …

2. The boy suggests hiring some … there.

3. Which five things do they plan to buy to eat? Choose from the following list.

Cooked sausage
Yoghurt
Pâté
Ham
Salad
Cheese
Bread
Oranges
Peaches
Melon

Exercise 4.2 A la boulangerie

Listen to the CD track and then write your answers in English.

1. The customer buys two …

2. The customer buys … chocolate rolls.

3. The apple tart costs … euros.

4. The total cost is … euros and … cents.

Exercise 4.3 Au restaurant

Listen to the CD track and then write your answers in English.

1. Which ingredients make up a Coupe Liégeoise? Choose from the following list.

   Banana

   Nuts

   Coffee ice cream

   Apple

   Whipped cream

   Meringue

   Chocolate sauce

2. The boy does not have Coupe Liégeoise because he doesn't like …

3. The boy orders … instead.

Exercise 5.1 Au syndicat d'initiative

Listen to the CD track and decide whether the following sentences are true or false.

1. The town plan shows all the main buildings of the town.

2. The man mentions a castle, a museum and a swimming pool.

3. The castle is open on Mondays.

4. The castle has free entry.

5. A visit to the castle takes at least two hours.

Exercise 5.2 A la gare

Listen to the CD track and decide whether the following sentences are true or false.

1. The girl wants to travel to Toulouse today.

2. She would prefer to travel in the morning.

3. The 10:20 train arrives in Toulouse at 13:00.

4. She will have to change trains.

5. She asks for a seat in the smoking section.

Exercise 5.3 Au téléphone

Listen to the CD track and decide whether the following sentences are true or false.

1. Anne is arriving in Nice tomorrow.

2. She will arrive at 8:20.

3. Jean-Marc advises Anne to take a taxi.

4. They agree to meet at the station exit.

Exercise 6.1 On achète des glaces

Listen to the CD track and then choose one of the four possible answers to each question:

1. How many flavours of ice cream are available?
   (a) Two
   (b) Three
   (c) Four
   (d) Five

2. Which flavour would the boy have preferred?
   (a) Strawberry
   (b) Pistachio
   (c) Coffee
   (d) Chocolate

3. Which flavour does the boy buy for his friend?
   (a) Chocolate
   (b) Vanilla
   (c) Pistachio
   (d) Coffee

4. How much do the ice creams cost?
   (a) Two euros
   (b) Three euros
   (c) Four euros
   (d) Five euros

5. What does the boy realise?
   (a) He has left his wallet at the hotel
   (b) Someone has stolen his wallet
   (c) He can't find his friend
   (d) He doesn't have enough money

Exercise 6.2 On va en ville

Listen to the CD track and then choose one of the four possible answers to each question:

1. Where does the boy suggest they go that afternoon?
   (a) The cinema
   (b) The swimming pool
   (c) The beach
   (d) The theatre

2. Why doesn't the girl want to go there?
   (a) It's too cold
   (b) She has no money
   (c) She can't swim
   (d) She finds it boring

3. What do they decide to do in town?
   (a) Buy a present for the boy's brother
   (b) Go to the café
   (c) Buy some food for a picnic
   (d) Go the the library

4. What time is the bus into town?
   (a) 10:15
   (b) 12:00
   (c) 1:15
   (d) 15:01

Exercise 6.3 Au cinéma

Listen to the CD track and then choose one of the four possible answers to each question:

1. At what times is the film being shown today?
   - (a) 13:00 and 16:00
   - (b) 14:30 and 18:30
   - (c) 15:00 and 18:30
   - (d) 15:15 and 20:30

2. What time does the first showing end?
   - (a) 15:45
   - (b) 17:20
   - (c) 17:45
   - (d) 20:00

3. How old is the girl?
   - (a) 13
   - (b) 14
   - (c) 15
   - (d) 16

4. How much do they pay for their tickets?
   - (a) 8 euros
   - (b) 10 euros
   - (c) 12 euros
   - (d) 14 euros

5. What does the girl ask?
   - (a) Where the refreshments are
   - (b) Where the screens are
   - (c) Where the box office is
   - (d) Where the toilets are

Exercise 7.1 A l'hôtel

Listen to the CD track and then answer the questions in English.

1. How many nights has M. Duclos booked?
2. Which rooms has his family been given?
3. Where are these rooms exactly?
4. What is the advantage of these rooms?
5. Where is the lift located?
6. When is breakfast served?
7. Where is the dining-room?

Exercise 7.2 A la plage

Listen to the CD track and then answer the questions in English.

1. What is the first thing the boy says?
2. What has he lost?
3. What does the girl suggest he may have done?
4. Where does he find it?
5. Who goes to buy the ice creams?

Exercise 7.3 Au téléphone

Listen to the CD track and then answer the questions in English.

1. Where is Sylvie?
2. What does her mother say about when she will be back?
3. What message does Julien leave for her?
4. When can Sylvie ring him?
5. Why will he be at home at that time?

Exercise 7.4 Une Française à Londres

Listen to the CD track and then answer the questions in English.

1. What is the girl's first question?
2. What does the boy not know?
3. What does he know?
4. Give the precise directions that the boy gives her.

Exercise 7.5 Au restaurant

Listen to the CD track and then answer the questions in English.

1. What does the girl say she is about to do?
2. What do they discuss and what is the outcome?

Exercise 7.6 On choisit un cadeau

Listen to the CD track and then answer the questions in English.

1. Why has the boy come into the shop?
2. What is the first item he looks at?
3. Why does he particularly like it?
4. How much is it?
5. Why is it so expensive?
6. How much does he pay for the item he finally chooses?

Reading

How the examination works

Instructions will be given in English. There will be 25 questions on a number of short passages (usually arranged in five or six sections). There will be several exercises of differing length, covering a range of different approaches to the development of reading skills, for example: gap-filling, multiple choice, matching headlines to texts, matching pictures to descriptions, matching two halves of a sentence, matching questions and answers, matching people and opinions, choosing a number of correct answers from a list, answering questions in French (marked for communication only). There will be one section with questions and answers in English.

Exercise 8.1

Michel is talking about a typical day. Copy the passage and choose a word from the box below to fill each gap, as in the example:

Je … **m'appelle** … Michel. J'ai treize ans.

Bon, normalement, le … je vais à l'école en … avec papa. Il conduit assez vite. Il a beaucoup de … à faire, et on quitte la … toujours en retard. Au collège cette année je suis en sixième, donc on a deux heures d'… par semaine.

Moi j'aime ça, car je suis … en langues. Le mardi on a cinq cours, dont maths, chimie, anglais, … et histoire-géo.

On … assez bien à la cantine, il y a toujours quelque chose que j'aime et on peut choisir. Mon … de latin est très amiable, mais je n'aime pas mon prof de musique: il nous fait … !

fort	maison	prof	~~m'appelle~~	anglais	latin	forte	travailler	route
voiture	mange	suis	sciences	matin	vélo	fenêtre		

24

Exercise 8.2

Read the following text, and answer the questions below:

Marianne

En France presque tous les écoliers sont externes. Ils arrivent à l'école le matin, et rentrent à la maison tous les soirs. Moi, je suis donc exceptionnelle! Je suis pensionnaire parce que mon père est militaire, alors nous changeons de domicile tous les deux ans. Quand mon père revient après une absence de quelques mois, on fête son arrivée!

Magali

Au collège, je suis un peu triste le week-end, car nous ne sommes pas nombreuses dans le pensionnat, mais les surveillantes qui restent pour nous garder sont très gentilles. On n'a pas le droit de sortir en ville le week-end, mais on s'amuse assez bien entre nous.

Stéphane

Ça fait un an et demi que je suis pensionnaire à Lyon, parce que l'école près de notre ferme n'existe plus. Je n'aime pas vivre comme ça, et j'écris toutes les semaines à mon père pour lui demander de trouver une solution. Je rentre chez moi tous les week-ends, mais c'est de plus en plus difficile de repartir le dimanche soir.

Patrick

J'adore rester à l'école le week-end. J'ai de très bons copains et on joue au foot ou au basket ensemble, et il y a plein d'autres choses à faire. Il y a des surveillants qui sont assez sympa. On mange bien et on regarde des tas de trucs à la télé. J'ai l'impression qu'on nous plaint, mais il ne faut pas. Moi, ça va!

Who says what? Decide whether Marianne, Magali, Stéphane or Patrick makes each of these statements:

1. Dans l'ensemble, j'aime mon collège.

2. Mon école a fermé ses portes il y a dix-huit mois.

3. La cuisine à mon école est assez bonne.

4. J'aimerais aller au cinéma le samedi soir, mais c'est interdit.

5. Mon père est officier de l'armée de l'air.

6. Notre famille déménage relativement souvent.

7. Je m'intéresse aux sports.

8. A notre collège on a le droit de regarder la télévision.

9. Je m'amuse avec mes copains.

10. Je n'aime pas me séparer de mes parents toutes les semaines.

Exercise 8.3

Read the following text and decide which advert answers each question.

Tu as douze ans. Tu n'es pas très fort(e) en maths. Tu lis le journal régional pour trouver des cours particuliers le week-end. Voici des annonces.

Cours et leçons

(a)

PROF DE LATIN pour adultes région Nantes donne cours privés tous niveaux. Se déplace. 20 €/h

(b)

DONNE COURS de français: Jeune étudiante niveau bac+ donne cours aux élèves de 6e 5e préparation examens. 17€/h

(c)

MATHÉMATICIEN PROF expérimenté donne cours aux étudiant(e)s bac prép. entrée univ. 25€/heure

(d)

JH ÉTUDIANT donne cours de mathématiques tous niveaux, tous âges, réussite assurée 18€/h

(e)

ANGLAISE RETRAITÉE donne leçons d'anglais. Ancien prof en Ecosse.

(f)

JF DONNE cours de mathématiques aux lycéen(ne)s le mercredi. 22€/h

1. Quel professeur vas-tu choisir?

2. Ton oncle veut se perfectionner en latin. Y a-t-il un prof pour lui?

3. Ta cousine est nulle en français! Quelle annonce doit-elle lire?

4. Je veux suivre des cours de maths, mais je ne suis pas libre le week-end. Quelle annonce dois-je lire?

5. Lequel des professeurs n'est pas français?

Vocabulary	
le cours particulier	one-to-one private lesson
privé	private
le niveau	level, standard
le bac (baccalauréat)	exam, equivalent of A levels
le bac+	study after A level
JH (jeune homme)	young man
réussite assurée	success guaranteed
JF (jeune femme)	young woman
le lycéen, la lycéenne	secondary school student

Exercise 8.4

Marie-Annick is talking about her weekend.

Copy the passage and choose a word from the box below to fill each gap, as in the example:

Je … **suis** … Marie-Annick. J'ai treize ans.

D'habitude, je … le week-end à faire des activités sportives en plein air. Quand il fait beau, je déteste … à l'intérieur. Je joue … avec mes deux … frères, qui ont six et quatre ans.

S'il pleut on fait des … de société ou on regarde un DVD dans le … Je suis fanatique de dessins animés: mon père me dit que je suis toujours un bébé mais ça m'est égal!

Quelquefois j'aide ma mère à préparer le déjeuner. Elle ne refuse … un coup de main, parce qu'il y a toujours beaucoup de … à table le dimanche. Mes cousins habitent tout … et ils viennent manger chez nous. On va chez … le samedi soir.

---

monde	~~suis~~	souvent	rester	me reposer	près	presque	salon
cuisine	eux	jeux	heure	petit	passe	petits	jamais

27

Exercise 8.5

You have received an email. Read the message, then answer the questions in English.

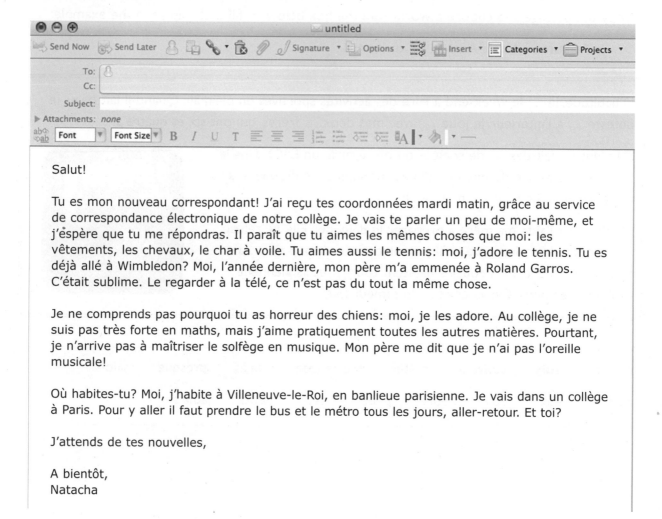

Salut!

Tu es mon nouveau correspondant! J'ai reçu tes coordonnées mardi matin, grâce au service de correspondance électronique de notre collège. Je vais te parler un peu de moi-même, et j'espère que tu me répondras. Il paraît que tu aimes les mêmes choses que moi: les vêtements, les chevaux, le char à voile. Tu aimes aussi le tennis: moi, j'adore le tennis. Tu es déjà allé à Wimbledon? Moi, l'année dernière, mon père m'a emmenée à Roland Garros. C'était sublime. Le regarder à la télé, ce n'est pas du tout la même chose.

Je ne comprends pas pourquoi tu as horreur des chiens: moi, je les adore. Au collège, je ne suis pas très forte en maths, mais j'aime pratiquement toutes les autres matières. Pourtant, je n'arrive pas à maîtriser le solfège en musique. Mon père me dit que je n'ai pas l'oreille musicale!

Où habites-tu? Moi, j'habite à Villeneuve-le-Roi, en banlieue parisienne. Je vais dans un collège à Paris. Pour y aller il faut prendre le bus et le métro tous les jours, aller-retour. Et toi?

J'attends de tes nouvelles,

A bientôt,
Natacha

1. Is Natacha's correspondent a boy or a girl?

2. Name two of Natacha's free-time interests.

3. What is her worst subject at school?

4. What, does Natacha suggest, is the French equivalent of Wimbledon?

5. What happened last year?

6. What were Natacha's impressions of this event?

7. What fact clearly surprised Natacha?

8. Why does her father think she is tone-deaf?

9. Where is Villeneuve-le-Roi?

10. How does she get to school every day?

Exercise 8.6

Véronique is talking about her holiday and her animals.

Copy the passage and choose a word from the box below to fill each gap, as in the example.

> Je m'appelle Véronique. J'ai … **quatorze** … ans.

Ma destination … de vacances, c'est l'Italie. On y est … l'année dernière et c'était épatant. J'ai des amis qui … que visiter les monuments historiques, c'est nul. Moi, ça m'intéresse beaucoup. On est allés à Rome, la capitale italienne, où j'ai pris des centaines de … avec mon appareil numérique!

On a vu le Forum Romain, la Fontaine de Trévi et bien d'autres choses. Mais pour moi le clou du séjour, c'était le Colisée. Dire qu'on l'a construit … deux mille …, c'est incroyable.

Pour nous, le problème quand on veut … en vacances, c'est de trouver quelqu'un pour s'occuper de garder les animaux. Dans ma famille on a deux chiens et un chat. Il faut les … en …, et ça je trouve difficile. Si on … pour seulement une semaine, c'est ma grand-mère qui vient s'en occuper.

---

mettre	photos	part	~~quatorze~~	photo	pense	préférée
il y a	aller	allés	pension	ans	pensent	onze	préférer

Exercise 8.7

Camping-Caravaning
LE PARADIS

85 Ste-Hermine, France

Bienvenue dans notre camping!

TARIF 2009   **par 24 h**

Emplacement tente moyenne (2 à 6 pers.) €6,00

Emplacement petite tente (1 à 2 pers.) €4,50

Emplacement caravane €9,50

Branchement électrique €2,00

NOS SERVICES:

Bloc sanitaire (WCs, lavabos, douches, lave-linge) ouvert 24h/24h.

Restaurant ouvert de 12 h à 15 h et de 19 h à 23 h tous les jours sauf le mercredi soir.

Salle de jeux (tennis de table, babyfoot) ouvert toute la journée jusqu'à 22 h.

Alimentation à la réception, ouvert de 7 h à 11 h 45 et de 15 h à 20 h tous les jours.

Boulangerie A commander à la réception pour le lendemain.

Afin de respecter le calme des autres, nous vous demandons d'éteindre vos radio et poste de télévision dès 23 h.

Les chiens doivent être tenus en laisse

Merci et bonnes vacances!

La Direction

You are on holiday in France. You are spending a week with your parents, brother and sister on a campsite near the sea. Here is the brochure of the Le Paradis campsite. Read the brochure and answer the questions in English.

1. How much would it cost for a caravan with electricity supply for one night?

2. How much would your family have to pay for one night with a tent?

3. Which facilities can be used at any time at all?

4. Is it possible to have lunch at the restaurant on Wednesday?

5. Where would you find basic general supplies?

6. What do you need to do to get bread?

7. What are you supposed to do after 11.00 pm?

8. For how much of the day could you play table football if you wanted?

9. Why do you get the impression that the campsite management have had problems with dogs in the past?

Vocabulary

un emplacement	pitch (for a tent or caravan)
le branchement	connection
le lavabo	wash-basin
jusqu'à	until
l'alimentation (f.)	everyday necessities, general supplies, grocery
commander	to order
afin de	in order to
éteindre	to turn off (electric appliances)
dès	from, starting at, as from
tenir en laisse	to keep on a lead

Exercise 8.8

Read this extract from a tourist guide to Avignon.

Notre tour comprend une visite guidée tous les jours pendant votre séjour. Nous vous proposons le Pont Saint Bénézet (plus connu sous le nom «Le Pont d'Avignon»), le Palais des Papes, la rue des Tinturiers, et le rocher des Doms …

La réalité du Pont Saint Bénézet contredit les paroles de la chanson «Sur le Pont d'Avignon». Ce n'était pas possible de danser en rond, parce qu'il n'y avait pas assez de place – le pont était trop étroit. On pense maintenant qu'on a dansé à l'auberge située sous le pont au pied d'un pilier.

Après notre visite du pont, nous emprunterons une des petites rues de la vieille ville pour nous rendre au Palais des Papes, où les maîtres de l'église romaine ont demeuré de 1309 à 1378. C'est un des papes qui a acheté ce palais à la Comtesse de Provence: le palais a été rendu à la France en 1791.

In the text, find the French expressions for these phrases:

1. our tour includes

2. every day of your stay

3. contradicts the words of the song

4. enough room

5. too narrow

6. it is now thought

7. at the base of a pillar

8. the old town

9. to go (literally, to get ourselves)

10. was given back.

Exercise 8.9

Read the passage in Exercise 8.8 and answer these questions in English:

1. How often is there a guided tour?
2. What is the more correct name for the Pont d'Avignon?
3. Why is the traditional story of the dancing on the bridge in some doubt?
4. Where is it now thought that the dancing happened?
5. Which route will the tour take after the bridge?
6. Why was the palace known as the Palace of the Popes?
7. What happened in 1791?

Exercise 8.10

Paul is talking about his house.

Copy the passage and choose a word from the box to fill each gap, as in the example:

Je m'appelle Paul. J'ai treize ans. J'habite à ... **Troyes** ...

Depuis l'... de trois ans, j'habite ici à Troyes. C'est une ville historique et intéressante. Il faut absolument passer par ici si vous ... dans la région de Champagne. Ma mère est ... ici, pourtant mon père vient de Perpignan. La maison que j'habite est vieille. On l'a construite en 1875. J'ai des amis qui ... venir chez moi, surtout qu'ils habitent des quartiers où il n'y a que des pavillons modernes.

Au ... étage il y a trois chambres, dont la mienne et la chambre de mes parents. Je ... ma chambre avec mon frère Matthieu. La chambre de ma soeur est au deuxième étage ainsi que celle de ... grand-mère. A côté de la chambre de ... parents se trouve le bureau de mon père. Mon père est notaire. Il passe beaucoup de ... à travailler à la maison, même le ...

partage	~~Troyes~~	adorent	mon	être	êtes	chambre	ma
âge	née	soir	premier	ans	heures	temps	mes	partagent

32

Vocabulary

par ici	this way
pourtant	however, and yet
surtout que	especially since, especially as
un pavillon	small suburban house, bungalow
dont	of which
ainsi que	as well as
un notaire	lawyer (similar to solicitor)

Exercise 8.11

Read the passage, and then decide whether the statements below are true or false.

> Je suis Stéphane. J'habite à Lille, dans le nord industriel de la France. L'année dernière on est allés au bord de la mer, mais j'aime mieux aller à la montagne, où on peut faire tant de différentes choses. La montagne, ce n'est pas seulement pour ceux qui aiment la neige: en été on peut y découvrir un monde de nature et de beauté. Il y a deux ans, mon père nous a emmenés dans les Pyrénées, près de la frontière espagnole. Cette année-là, mes amis qui avaient décidé de prendre leurs vacances au bord de la mer avait souffert d'une chaleur exceptionnelle, qu'on appelle une 'canicule', tandis que nous, on avait pu faire des promenades et des randonnées presque tous les jours. Ma soeur et mon père avaient été ravis de découvrir des fleurs et des plantes dont ils ignoraient l'existence auparavant, et moi, je m'étais contentée de respirer l'air frais en faisant du VTT sur les petits sentiers de forêt et de me baigner dans la piscine de l'hôtel en redescendant des collines. J'avais eu pour compagnie deux garçons français de mon âge – j'ai treize ans – et un 'grand' Andorran de quinze ans qui nous avait initiés aux merveilles de cette région comme sa forêt, ses animaux sauvages et ses paysages sans pareil. De plus, il parlait couramment trois langues!
>
> De retour à la maison je m'étais juré de revenir au plus tôt possible.

1. Stéphane habite au bord de la mer.

2. Stéphane est allé à la plage l'année dernière.

3. C'est une bonne idée d'aller à la montagne en été.

4. Stéphane trouve que les paysages de montagne sont beaux.

5. On y trouve les mêmes fleurs et les mêmes plantes qu'à Lille.

6. Le père de Stéphane apprécie la nature.

7. A l'hôtel ce n'était pas possible de faire de la natation.

8. L'Andorran était plus âgé que Stéphane.

9. L'Andorran connaissait bien la région où Stéphane est allé en vacances.

10. Stéphane voudrait retourner bientôt dans les Pyrénées.

Note: Vocabulary follows on next page.

Vocabulary

aimer mieux	to like better, to prefer
tant (de)	so much, so many
souffrir	to suffer
la chaleur	heat
exceptionnel	exceptional
la canicule	heatwave
tandis que	while
auparavant	beforehand
le sentier	path
un Andorran	Andorran (someone from Andorra)
le paysage	countryside, landscape
sans pareil	without equal
jurer	to swear

Exercise 8.12

Philippe is talking about what he does with his pocket money.

Copy the passage and choose a word from the box to fill each gap, as in the example:

Je vais en ville par le … **train** …

Salut! Moi, j'habite un hameau à 10 kilomètres de Saintes, donc quand je suis libre, j'aime aller en ville parce qu'il n'y a pas … magasins là où j'habite. Je m'appelle Philippe. J'ai deux frères, Alex et Thomas, qui … treize et neuf ans. Moi, j'ai quinze ans. J'adore la chanson française: c'est un style de musique uniquement français, qui mélange la musique et la poésie. A Saintes il y a beaucoup de magasins où on peut acheter des CDs de ce genre. J'aime … Georges Brassens. A l'école, on nous a fait écouter sa chanson «le Petit Cheval Blanc» et j'ai tout de suite … acheter le CD. Maintenant je préfère télécharger de la musique de l'internet avec mon lecteur MP3. C'est plus … et moins cher.

D'habitude, je vais en ville acheter des vêtements. J'aide ma mère à la maison. Pour ça, elle … donne vingt euros tous les quinze jours. Ce n'est pas beaucoup, mais je nettoie aussi les voitures de nos voisins et je peux acheter ce qu'il me … ainsi que des cadeaux de Noël. Je ne m'intéresse pas … sport, mais quelquefois je vais au cinéma: je me passionne pour les films d'avant-guerre en noir et … On peut les regarder à la maison sur DVD, mais au cinéma il y a une ambiance tout à fait …

de	sont	ont	pratique	voulu	me	des	spécial	
surtout	au	aux	fait	faut	~~train~~	blanc	spéciale	

34

Vocabulary

un hameau	hamlet
la chanson française	traditional French songs
uniquement	only, uniquely
mélanger	to mix
la poésie	poetry
pratique	practical
d'avant-guerre	pre-war
une ambiance	an atmosphere
spécial	different, special

Exercise 8.13

After the holidays, you receive postcards from some of your French friends. Match up each postcard with the descriptions of each person.

Antoinette   Etudiante très sérieuse et travailleuse, qui aime l'histoire et le soleil.

Véronique   Fille sportive qui déteste le mauvais temps.

Georges   Lycéen qui travaille assez bien mais qui passe beaucoup de temps à practiquer son instrument à cordes.

Marc   Collégien de Nantes, il a un frère et une soeur plus âgés que lui. Il n'aime pas beaucoup regarder les vieux films.

Marie-Claire   Fille d'un fermier, Marie-Claire ne va pas souvent en ville, mais cette année, elle aurait bien aimé visiter à la capitale.

1.

Salut! On se régale ici! On fait des tas de trucs mais ce que j'aime le plus ce sont les randonnées. Il fait assez chaud, mais pas trop. Il n'a pas plu une seule fois, heureusement.

Ciao! ...

2.

Bonjour! Tu vas bien? C'est la première fois que je suis venue à Paris! C'est extra mais la circulation, c'est incroyable! On se verra à Noël, n'est-ce pas?

xx ...

3.

Salut, nous voici à Toulouse! Je suis avec Tony et Sonia. Nos parents sont allés au ciné, nous on se repose dans un café - c'est fatigant le shopping!!

Bisous, ...

4.

Mon cher Charles,

Tu aimerais cette ville: beaucoup de touristes mais aussi beaucoup de choses à faire et à voir. Le bâtiment historique que j'ai le plus aimé, c'est le Palais des Papes. Il fait très chaud, mais moi, ça m'est égal.

A bientôt, ...

5.

Un mot de l'aéroport en attendant le départ de notre vol. Chez le marchand de journaux j'ai trouvé plein de magazines de musique. J'ai choisi «Guitariste». C'était assez cher mais très intéressant.

A plus, ...

Vocabulary

un(e) lycéen(ne)	secondary school student
un instrument à cordes	stringed instrument
un(e) collégien(ne)	11- to 14-year-old pupil
se régaler	to have a really good time
des tas de trucs	loads of stuff
incroyable	incredible
ça m'est égal	it's all the same to me, I don't mind
plein de	plenty of

Exercise 8.14

Read this extract from an article in a French regional newspaper.

Vol à l'improviste aux Hirondelles

UN CAMBRIOLEUR est entré par la porte-fenêtre du salon, qui donne sur un balcon de 5 ou 6 mètres carrés. Il est fort probable qu'il s'est introduit de cette façon facilement, car le propriétaire ne peut se souvenir s'il avait fermé cette porte-fenêtre à clé ou non.

Monsieur Gainsbourg, propriétaire de l'appartement du premier étage de l'immeuble aux Hirondelles, dans un quartier où le calme est rarement interrompu, regrette d'avoir laissé tout ce qu'il venait d'acheter au milieu du plancher du salon ce matin même, puis d'être tout de suite sorti pour aller chercher sa fille à l'aéroport. En rentrant, deux heures plus tard, il a trouvé la porte d'entrée ouverte et a deviné tout de suite ce qui s'était passé. Il n'a pas laissé entrer sa fille, qui a téléphoné à la police immédiatement sur son portable.

On a interrogé les voisins du palier et les quelques habitants du quartier qui n'étaient pas partis en vacances, mais personne n'a pu éclairer cet incident. La nature des objets volés (un lecteur, des disques, des livres et magazines, même une trompette japonaise), laisse à supposer que le criminel s'intéresse à la musique.

In the text, find the French expressions for these phrases:

1. it is nonetheless likely
2. he used this means of entry
3. owner of the flat
4. regrets having left
5. that he'd just bought
6. to fetch his daughter
7. what had happened
8. he did not let his daughter go in
9. the type of items stolen
10. leads one to believe.

Vocabulary	
à l'improviste	opportunistic
le cambrioleur	burglar
la porte-fenêtre	the 'French windows'
carré	square
au milieu de	in the middle of
ce matin même	that same morning
le palier	the landing
éclairer	to shed light on

Exercise 8.15

Read the passage in Exercise 8.14 and answer these questions in English:

1. How did the burglar get in?
2. What does the title tell us about how well planned the burglary was?
3. What was the owner unsure of?
4. What does the owner say he now regrets?
5. Why did he hurry off from the flat?
6. Why were only a few local residents available to be interviewed?
7. What had the stolen items in common with each other?

Exercise 8.16

Joséphine is talking about her birthday.

Copy the passage and choose a word from the box to fill each gap, as in the example:

Salut. Moi je m'appelle Joséphine. Cette … **année** … j'ai fêté mon treizième anniversaire.

J'ai reçu trois livres. Ma tante Julie sait que j'adore …, donc j'ai reçu trois livres de sa part. Ils étaient magnifiques, pleins de … de chiens et de chevaux.

Nous, à la maison, on a deux chiens qui s'appellent Mézi et Chouchou. Ils sont adorables mais ils ne sont pas très intelligents! Le jour de mon anniversaire ma mère m'a … à sept heures et demie. Si je dormais toujours, c'est que la veille j'étais allée à une boum chez ma … amie Tochiko. On a écouté des CDs et on a dansé. On a bien mangé aussi. C'était …! Tout le monde était de bonne humeur et on est restés jusqu'à une heure du matin. Ma mère ne s'inquiétait pas, parce que le père de Tochiko était … tout le temps, et c'est lui qui m'a reconduite à la maison en … après la boum. J'étais fatiguée mais … le lendemain matin!

Mes parents m'attendaient pour le petit déjeuner. Ils m'ont fait la surprise quand je suis descendue, en m'offrant mon cadeau – une année d'abonnement au centre équestre de … village!

---

formidable	trois	voiture	année	~~années~~	réveillée	lire	mieux
meilleure	photo	la	là	heures	heureuse	photos	notre

Exercise 8.17

Read this passage and answer the questions in English.

Le quatorze juillet j'ai appelé mon copain Patrick pour l'inviter à venir chez nous le soir. On fait toujours la fête, le 14 juillet. Ça fait longtemps que mon père invite tous les voisins à nous rejoindre dans le jardin pour un barbecue qui est la façon dont on commence la soirée. On apporte des viandes et d'autres plats, et c'est maman qui organise ce qu'on va manger avant de donner tout à papa pour le barbecue. Naturellement, c'est lui qui s'occupe de la cuisson à l'extérieur. On reçoit d'habitude une vingtaine de personnes, mais cette année il y en a eu trente-deux!

Après le repas, qui dure généralement de vingt heures à minuit, tout le monde rentre les tables et les chaises dans la véranda, et on sort dans la rue pour assister aux grands feux d'artifice du village.

Il y a un orchestre et on danse sur la place du village. Le lendemain, le silence règne partout, et papa ne se lève habituellement qu'à midi! Patrick a eu du mal à partir à la fin, tellement il s'était amusé. Il a dit qu'il n'y a jamais rien dans son village, le 14 juillet. C'est dommage!

1. Why did the writer telephone his friend?
2. Which part of the evening is the barbecue?
3. Who provides the food for the barbecue?
4. Where is the barbecue held?
5. Who organises what will be eaten?
6. What does Dad do?
7. How many people usually come to this event?
8. How many people came this year?
9. What does everyone help with after the meal?
10. Describe the scene the following morning.

Writing

Question 1 exercises

How the examination operates

Question 1 will require the writing of five simple sentences in French, each based on a visual or written stimulus. Candidates should write five to ten words on each stimulus. Marks will be awarded for content, accuracy and quality of language.

Exercise 9.1

Write a sentence in French for each of the pictures below, as in the example:

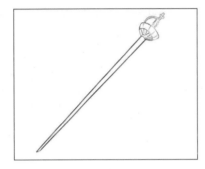

Hier j'ai fait de l'escrime: c'était passionnant.

1.

2.

3.

4.

5.

Exercise 9.2

Write a sentence in French for each of the pictures below, as in the example:

A Pâques nous sommes allés à l'Arc de Triomphe: c'était incroyable.

1.

2.

3.

4.
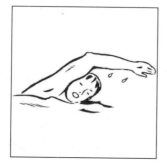

5.

Exercise 9.3

Write a sentence in French for each of the pictures below, as in the example:

Ma soeur aime faire du patin avec ses copines.

1.

2.

3.

4.

5.

Exercise 9.4

Write a sentence in French for each of the pictures below, as in the example:

Cette année nous allons faire du ski en Andorre.

1.

2.

3.

4.

5.

Exercise 9.5

Write a sentence in French for each of the pictures below, as in the example:

Ma mère a acheté des chaussures ce matin.

1.

2.

3.

4.

5.

Exercise 9.6

Write a sentence in French for each of the pictures below, as in the example:

Le quatorze juillet, on a fait un barbecue dans le jardin.

1.

2.

3.

4.

5.

Question 2 exercises

Exercise 10.1

You are visiting your French penfriend's school. Write a letter to your French teacher in the UK. Write between 80 and 130 words. You must mention at least **four** of the points below:

- la cuisine à l'école
- tes amis
- le sport à l'école
- un cours
- un problème

Exercise 10.2

You are in Avignon. Write a letter to the parents of your French penfriend. Write between 80 and 130 words. You must mention at least **four** of the points below:

- l'hôtel
- un repas
- la ville
- un monument
- un problème

Exercise 10.3

You are in London with your friends. It is raining, and you are in McDonald's. Write a letter to your French penfriend. Write between 80 and 130 words. You must mention at least **four** of the points below:

- ton voyage à Londres
- tes amis
- tes achats
- le temps
- un problème

Exercise 10.4

You are at home. Write a letter to your French penfriend. Write between 80 and 130 words. You must mention at least **four** of the points below:

- la ville
- ta routine
- ton argent de poche
- un cadeau
- un sport

Exercise 10.5

You are in your room at home. You decide to write your diary entry for today in French. Write between 80 and 130 words. You must mention at least **four** of the points below:

- les activités ce matin
- les repas
- une fête ou une boum cet après-midi
- le temps
- tes amis

Exercise 10.6

You are camping in France. Write a letter to a friend. Write between 80 and 130 words. You must mention at least **four** of the points below:

- le temps
- ton voyage
- le site du camping
- les autres gens
- les activités

Exercise 10.7

Write an email to the Hôtel de Paris to make a reservation. Write between 80 and 130 words. You must mention at least **four** of the points below:

- les dates de votre réservation
- les autres gens
- la chambre
- le prix
- les repas

Exercise 10.8

You are spending eight days in a luxury hotel on the Côte d'Azur. Write a letter to a friend. Write between 80 and 130 words. You must mention at least **four** of the points below:

- l'hôtel
- un repas
- le temps
- la ville
- les activités

Exercise 10.9

You are on holiday in the Alps. Write a letter to a friend. Write between 80 and 130 words. You must mention at least **four** of the points below:

- l'hôtel
- un repas
- la ville
- les activités
- un problème

Exercise 10.10

Write an email to your cousins in Biarritz to announce your arrival there, and arrange a meeting. Write between 80 and 130 words. You must mention at least **four** of the points below:

- la ville
- l'hôtel
- les monuments
- les activités
- le temps

Exercise 10.11

Your penfriend asks what you normally do in the evenings after school. What would you reply? Write between 80 and 130 words. You must mention at least **four** of the points below:

- les cours
- les professeurs
- le repas
- tes amis
- les activités

Appendix

List of topics covered by the ISEB Common Entrance syllabus

- Language of the classroom, including basic ICT
- House, home, daily routine and chores
- Life and work at school
- Time, dates, numbers and prices
- Personal description
- Family, friends and pets
- Meeting people
- Free-time activities
- Describing holiday activities
- Visiting a café or restaurant
- Simple health problems
- Description of a town or region
- Finding the way and using public transport
- Understanding tourist information
- Shopping (e.g. for food, clothes, presents) and pocket money
- Weather

Also available from Galore Park

English
Junior English 1
Junior English 1 Answers
Junior English 2
Junior English 2 Answers
Junior English 3
Junior English 3 Answers
So you really want to learn English 1
So you really want to learn English 1 Answers
So you really want to learn English 2
So you really want to learn English 2 Answers
So you really want to learn English 3
So you really want to learn English 3 Answers
English Practice Exercises 11+
English Practice Exercises 11+ Answers
English Practice Exercises 13+
English Practice Exercises 13+ Answers
English ISEB Revision Guide
English Year 9

Mathematics
Junior Maths 1
Junior Maths 1 Answers
Junior Maths 1 Teacher's Resource
Junior Maths 2
Junior Maths 2 Answers
Junior Maths 2 Teacher's Resource
Junior Maths 3
Junior Maths 3 Answers
So you really want to learn Maths 1
So you really want to learn Maths 1 Answers
So you really want to learn Maths 1 Worksheets
So you really want to learn Maths 2
So you really want to learn Maths 2 Answers
So you really want to learn Maths 2 Worksheets
So you really want to learn Maths 3
So you really want to learn Maths 3 Answers
So you really want to learn Maths 3 Worksheets
Mathematics Questions at 11+ Book A
Mathematics Questions at 11+ Book A Answer Book
Mathematics Questions at 11+ Book B
Mathematics Questions at 11+ Book B Answer Book
Mixed Maths Exercises Year 6 Pupil Book
Mixed Maths Exercises Year 6 Answers
Mixed Maths Exercises Year 7 Pupil Book
Mixed Maths Exercises Year 7 Answers
Mixed Maths Exercises Year 8 (Lower) Pupil Book
Mixed Maths Exercises Year 8 (Lower) Answers
Mathematics ISEB Revision Guide
Mathematics Pocket Notes

Science
Junior Science 1
Junior Science 1 Answers
Junior Science 1 Teacher's Resource
Junior Science 2
Junior Science 2 Answers
Junior Science 2 Teacher's Resource
Junior Science 3
Junior Science 3 Answers
Junior Science 3 Teacher's Resource
So you really want to learn Science 1
So you really want to learn Science 1 Answers
*So you really want to learn Science 1
    Teacher's Resource*
So you really want to learn Science 2
So you really want to learn Science 2 Answers
*So you really want to learn Science 2
    Teacher's Resource*
Science Pocket Notes – Living Things
*Science Pocket Notes – Materials and Their
    Properties*
Science Pocket Notes – Physical Processes

Geography
So you really want to learn Geography 1
So you really want to learn Geography 1 Answers
So you really want to learn Geography 2
So you really want to learn Geography 2 Answers
Geography ISEB Revision Guide
*Revision Crosswords for Common Entrance and
    Scholarship Geography*

History
Junior History 1
Junior History 1 Answers
Junior History 2
Junior History 2 Answers
Junior History 3
Junior History 3 Answers
So you really want to learn History 1
So you really want to learn History 1 Answers
So you really want to learn History 2
So you really want to learn History 2 Answers

Religious Studies
Religious Studies for Today
Bible Stories for Today
Religious Studies ISEB Revision
Preparing for Common Entrance Religious Studies

IPG Education Publisher of the Year 2009

Also available from Galore Park

Classics
So you really want to learn Latin I
So you really want to learn Latin I Answers
So you really want to learn Latin II
So you really want to learn Latin II Answers
So you really want to learn Latin III
So you really want to learn Latin III Answers
So you really want to learn Latin Translations
Latin Prep 1
Latin Prep 1 Answers
Latin Prep 1 Audio
Latin Prep 2
Latin Prep 2 Answers
Latin Prep 3
Latin Prep 3 Answers
Latin Prep 1 Workbook A
Latin Prep 1 Workbook B
Latin Prep 1 Workbook Answers
Latin Puzzles
Latin Practice Exercises Level 1
Latin Practice Exercises Level 1 Answers
Latin Practice Exercises Level 2
Latin Practice Exercises Level 2 Answers
Latin Practice Exercises Level 3
Latin Practice Exercises Level 3 Answers
Nil Desperandum
Latin Galore
Ab Initio – A Latin Reference Grammar
Latin Vocabulary for Key Stage 3 and
    Common Entrance
Latin Flash Cards
A Latin Revision Reference for Common Entrance
    Level 1
A Latin Revision Reference for Common Entrance
    Level 2
The Jason Story – A Latin Reader
A Taste of Latin Poetry
Greek – A New Guide for Beginners

French
So you really want to learn French I
So you really want to learn French I Answers
So you really want to learn French I Audio
So you really want to learn French I Assessment Pack
So you really want to learn French 2
So you really want to learn French 2 Answers
So you really want to learn French 2 Audio
So you really want to learn French 2 Assessment Pack
So you really want to learn French 3
So you really want to learn French 3 Answers

So you really want to learn French 3 Audio
Skeleton French
French Vocabulary for Key Stage 3 and
    Common Entrance
Common Entrance French Grammar Handbook

Spanish
So you really want to learn Spanish I
So you really want to learn Spanish I Teacher's Book
So you really want to learn Spanish I Audio
So you really want to learn Spanish I Assessment Pack
So you really want to learn Spanish 2
So you really want to learn Spanish 2 Teacher's Book
So you really want to learn Spanish 2 Audio
So you really want to learn Spanish 3
So you really want to learn Spanish 3 Teacher's Book
So you really want to learn Spanish 3 Audio
Spanish Vocabulary for Key Stage 3 and
    Common Entrance

German
German Vocabulary for Key Stage 3 and
    Common Entrance
Und Du?

Study Skills
Study Skills – The complete guide to smart learning

Phonics
Step by Step Reading

**Learning Together Verbal and
Non Verbal Reasoning**
How to do Verbal Reasoning – A Step by Step Guide
Preparation for 11+ and 12+ Tests:
    Verbal Reasoning – Book 1
Preparation for 11+ and 12+ Tests:
    Verbal Reasoning – Book 2
Preparation for 11+ and 12+ Tests:
    Verbal Reasoning – Book 3
Preparation for 11+ and 12+ Tests:
    Verbal Reasoning – Book 4
Verbal Reasoning Challenge Tests
How to do Non Verbal Reasoning –
    A Step by Step Guide
Preparation for 11+ and 12+ Tests:
    Non Verbal Reasoning – Book 1
Preparation for 11+ and 12+ Tests:
    Non Verbal Reasoning – Book 2

IPG Education Publisher of the Year 2009